The New Series Canada

My *Broken* FAMILY

a novel

by

PAUL KROPP

H·I·P Books

New Series Canada

Copyright © 1989 and 2002 by Paul Kropp

National Library of Canada Cataloguing in Publication Data

Kropp, Paul 1948–
[split up]
    My Broken Family

(New Series Canada; 1)
Previously published under title: Split up.
ISBN 0-9731237-4-5

I. Title. II. Title: Split Up. III. Series.

PS 8571.R772S73 2002   jC813'.54   C2002-903559-7
PZ&

General editor: Paul Kropp
Text Design: Laura Brady
Illustrations redrawn by: Matt Melanson
Cover design: Robert Corrigan

  2 3 4 5 6 7   07 06 05

Printed and bound in Canada
High Interest Publishing is an imprint of the Chestnut Publishing Group

A divorce is always rotten. But sometimes it feels worse than rotten. When Maddy's parents split up, her whole life seems to fall apart. Maddy holds on to her dancing as the one thing that is really her own. But when the anger is finished, she finds that love is stronger than she thought.

CHAPTER 1

All Messed Up

I didn't see it coming. That's what they say, of course – that the kids never see it coming. But I still wasn't ready when they told me.

It wasn't fair – any of it. I had just come from my dance class, feeling tired but excited the way you do after dancing. It was one of those perfect October days. The leaves were just turning to yellow and orange. Kids were playing and shouting out on the street. My little brother, Jacob, yelled as he tore past me on his bike. Then he and his friend jumped off their bikes to play some kind of tag. From what I could see, it looked like Jacob was "it."

My father had to call Jacob three times before he would stop the game for supper. Then Jacob came charging into the house, the way he does. My mom yelled at him not slam the door. Of course,

Jacob let the door slam anyhow. Just like always.

For supper we had my dad's not-so-great meat-balls and sauce. The four of us ate like we always did. I was hungry, Dad dropped a meatball on the floor, and Mom kept telling Jacob to eat.

Jacob pushed the meatballs around on his plate, saying he didn't much like them. And Mom said he could have a peanut butter sandwich, but he had to eat at least *two* meatballs and "that was that." It all seemed so normal. It was like any other day in all the years since I'd been born.

When dinner was over, Jacob got up to go back to his friends outside. My mom wouldn't let him. She said, "Wait a minute – we've got something to talk about." Then she looked at my father, while he washed a pot at the sink.

"What's the matter?" Jacob asked. "Did I do something wrong?" He's only seven years old but he could hear the tone in Mom's voice as well as I could.

"No, it's nothing like that," she said, her hands folding and unfolding. "It's just that . . . well, your father and I have something we've got to tell you and Maddy." She looked at me, then quickly looked toward Dad again.

My father came away from the sink and sat down at the table. If I'd been looking at him, I would have known. I could have read it in his eyes. But how often do we ever look at parents? They're just supposed to be there – like couches and door-knobs. I mean, the last thing a kid should have to worry about is her family.

"This is a very difficult thing to explain . . . ," Dad began. And then he stopped, like he couldn't find the words.

My mom was silent. This is funny, because mostly she has lots to say. But now she just sat there, looking at my dad.

My dad cleared his throat and started again. "Well, you two may have noticed that there have been some problems between your mother and me. We haven't been getting along too well for some time no . . ." He paused, as if he couldn't quite catch his breath. "So . . . we've decided that the best thing would be . . . " and then his voice broke. He seemed about ready to cry.

My mom just shook her head, as if she were angry. "What he's trying to say is that we've decided to live apart."

"What?" I said. I heard their words, but I couldn't believe them.

"We've made up our minds that things just aren't working out for us," Mom said. She was still folding her hands over and over. "And your father wants a chance for a better life, on his own."

"That's not it," my dad said with sudden anger. I'd seen the anger and heard that voice before. But now my dad was trying hard to calm down, to seem like he was in control.

"Then what is it, Ed?" my mom asked. Her tone was cold, so cold.

"We've been talking about this – about our problems – for a very long time now. And we've tried," he said, looking for a second at Mom, "to get some help and work things out. But that didn't do any good, really. And the whole marriage has been going nowhere, so . . . " His voice died out.

Mom finished for him, "Your father is going to move out, into his own place."

Then there was silence. Jacob was still just sitting there, his mouth open, staring at the two of them. My mom had her mouth set, like she was trying hard not to cry. My dad looked down at the table, his hands gripping the edge of it.

"But where – ?" I began, then couldn't find the words to finish. *Where would we live?* was my question. *Maybe splitting up is fine for you, but what about us kids?*

My dad must have read my mind. "The two of you will be staying here with your mother, at least until the house is sold," he said.

"The house!" I shouted. "We have to move? Like splitting up isn't bad enough?"

"Calm down, Madison," my mother ordered. "This isn't easy for any of us."

I felt cold and confused. It was like this was some nightmare and pretty soon I'd wake up. My parents didn't fight, didn't even argue much. They'd never told us there was some kind of problem between them. It all seemed so crazy.

"The house won't sell right away, Maddy. And you and your mom will stay close and you won't

have to change schools, I hope. We haven't got all that worked out just yet."

"This stinks!" I said.

"Maddy!" my mother replied to shut me up.

And then we sat there, awkward with each other, as if we were strangers who'd just met on the street. It was all so cold, so controlled.

"Can't you go see a marriage counselor or something?" I said.

"We tried that, Maddy, but it didn't work," my

mother told me. Then there was silence again, that awful silence of shock and hurt and loss.

"It's not that we don't love you, or that our feelings for you are going to change any," Dad began. He was smiling at us, but the smile was a lie – a cover-up.

It was Jacob who broke him off. "Can I be excused?" he said, more polite than I had ever heard him.

"No," Dad replied in a very serious voice. "We've got too many things to talk about. You can't just go off to play when something like this has to be worked out."

"I don't want to play. I just – " but he couldn't finish. Tears came flooding from his eyes and his voice choked up. And then he was off, running from us, up the stairs to his room.

"You didn't handle that very well," my mom told Dad.

"I don't do this everyday, Diane. Maybe you think you could have handled it better –"

"Oh, stop it," I said, cutting them both off. I couldn't take them arguing with each other, not now, not after what they'd done. The two of them stared at me with that *look*, like somehow I was the one who had messed everything up.

That's when we all heard the crash from upstairs. Something smashed into pieces just over our heads.

CHAPTER 2

We'll Be Fine

I had just reached Jacob's room when there was a second crash, right against the door.

"Stop throwing stuff!" I yelled at him. "I'm coming in."

When I stuck my head inside Jacob's room, I could see bits of plastic smashed all over the floor. Jacob was on his bed, ready to throw another model against the door.

"What are you doing?" I said.

"I don't want these any more," he said. "I don't want any of this stuff any more, I just want –"

And then he broke into tears. His crying wasn't loud, but his whole body shook as the tears rolled down his cheeks.

"It'll be O.K.," I said, going over next to him on the bed. "Divorce isn't always the worst thing in the world. Shannon 's parents split up, and she came out of it all right." Shannon was the girl next door, my best friend.

"Yeah, but she's not *us*. It's not going to happen to *us*," Jacob said, still sniffling. He was trying to get himself back together to act tough. "I won't let it."

"You think smashing all those models you made with Dad is going to help? You think acting like a little brat is going to keep Mom and Dad together?" I asked him.

Jacob shook his head and lay back on the bed. He didn't have an answer – and neither did I.

"Look, Mom and Dad have got their own problems and somehow they have to work them out," I told him.

I sounded so wise, so mature for a fourteen-year-old. But that's only because it hadn't really hit me yet. Maybe that's what it means to be in shock – you don't feel anything because there's too much to feel all at once. I was cold and numb, almost like all this was happening to somebody else.

"What are we gonna do?" Jacob asked.

"We're going to go on living just like before," I said.

"But they're gonna sell the house."

"So it's just a house. We'll get another one, and it'll be the same except that Dad won't be here. He'll be at a new place and we'll get to stay over there sometimes." I tried to be upbeat, like this was some kind of great adventure.

"That sucks," Jacob said.

"You think everything sucks," I shot back at him. "Some kids say it's like having two houses. I know one girl, her dad bought a condo with a pool. She could go swimming when she went there for weekends."

Jacob waited for a second, thinking. It looked like he was weighing the pros and cons of the divorce. But looks can be deceiving. My brother was worried about something a lot bigger. "Maddy, you think maybe it was something *we* did?" he asked in a small voice.

"Don't be dumb," I told him. "It's nothing *we* did. Besides, there's always a chance they'll get back together," I said, trying to cheer him up.

"It's not final, not like a divorce. A lot of times, couples split up and get back together. There are people in Hollywood who get married and divorced over and over."

"Yeah, I guess," Jacob sighed, sitting up on the bed. His face brightened up so much that I had to keep going.

"Sure, it happens all the time," I told him – as if I really knew.

Neither of us said anything for a while. Jacob lay on his bed, staring at a poster of a skateboarder on the wall. I sat on his desk, listening to our parents below. They were arguing, of course. They were blaming each other for getting my little brother upset.

Then we heard my dad come tramping up the stairs, alone. He stopped at the bedroom door and hollered out, "You two all right?"

Of course, I lied and said, "We're fine." Not because we were, but because that's what I thought we were supposed to say.

My dad's footsteps went slowly down the hall to their room – I mean, my mom's room – and stopped. Maybe he was thinking about what to do. Then I heard him come back down the hall, knocking at Jacob's door.

"Can I come in?" he asked. It was as if he wasn't even welcome in our rooms any more.

"Yeah," Jacob shouted, sitting up on his bed. Somehow we all seemed so formal, like we had never been a family at all.

"I wanted to talk to you," my father said, looking down at the broken models on the floor. "Are you O.K., buddy?"

"Jus' fine," Jacob replied, covering up. We were both covering up, lying, holding back. We had to.

"I know this has to be a pretty tough thing for you two," he began. His voice was softer than it had been downstairs. "It's been pretty hard on your mother and me. I think if you only knew how hard we tried to keep our marriage together, well, maybe you'd understand."

"It's O.K., Dad," I told him. "We'll be fine, but where are you going to be?"

"I've got an apartment down on Donald Street," he explained.

"Is there a swimming pool?" Jacob asked. I could have killed him right about then.

My dad looked surprised. "I . . . I don't think so. It's not much really – only two bedrooms. So when you two come to stay I guess she gets the bed. You and I will have to bunk together."

"I can sleep on the couch, or even the floor," Jacob said, almost as if it would be like going camping.

"Well, I think we can find a way to work something out. There isn't a lot of money so things are going to be tight for a while. But I want you kids to know, despite what's happened," my dad's voice was choked up, "your mom and I love you very much."

"We know that, Dad," I said. And I think I really did know that – someplace deep down.

"Dad, do you really have to go?" Jacob asked. He was holding on to Dad and wouldn't let go. He had grabbed on to my dad's shirt, as if that might somehow make him stay with us and keep us all together.

"I've got to," Dad told him, pulling free, "I've got to."

When my dad stepped back, I could see the tears in his eyes. I'd never seen him cry before, not ever. But now he was standing in the doorway and tears were rolling down his cheeks. I think he wanted to say something, something more, but the words wouldn't come out. So he turned, hiding his face.

It took a second for him to find his voice. "Do

you think we can have a family hug," Dad asked, "just like always?"

"Sure," I said, putting one arm around Dad and one around my brother. The three of us hugged, just like we always did, except Mom wasn't part of it. And maybe that's what made it so awful.

CHAPTER 3

A Broken Angel

Two days later, a week before Halloween, Dad was gone. I remember the morning after he left, and how strange it felt. Somehow I thought Dad would still be there for breakfast, sitting in his chair just like always.

But there was an empty place at the table where Dad usually sat. None of us wanted to look there, to think about Dad not being with us. So we talked about school, and who had to do the dishes that day. My mom was up cleaning some shelves, a job I'd never seen her do before. She was smiling, trying hard to pretend that our lives were normal, like they used to be.

But they weren't, and that's what I tried to explain to Shannon. She was on my side, of course, but her kind of sympathy is a bit strange.

"What's normal?" Shannon said to me as we walked to school. "Normal went out with *That 70s Show*. My mom has had so many boyfriends since the divorce that I don't even bother to learn their names any more. And I haven't seen my dad in, like, five years. Is that normal?"

"That's weird," I said.

"Weird or sick, if you ask me," Shannon went on. "You guys just had it too easy," she said, stuffing her mouth with a hunk of chocolate. "Over half the families in the country have split up, sometimes more than once. You guys were the exceptions all along."

"Is that true?" I asked.

"True fact," she replied. "I did a report on divorce. All of us split families, we're the ones who are normal!" Shannon laughed with the silly giggle that sometimes drove me crazy.

"But my parents seemed O.K.," I said. "They never used to argue much. I mean, my dad would get angry sometimes, but I thought they loved each other."

"Maybe they do, but just can't live with each

other," Shannon said. "You remember when my mom had this guy Bob living with her? They looked like they loved each other a lot – I mean, they were all over each other. But when they weren't in love, they hated each other's guts. I told you about the night my Mom was going to slug Bob with a frying pan. They just didn't get along – like, totally."

"But my parents never fought," I told her. "They hardly even talked to each other."

"Well, maybe that's the problem. Either that, or one of your parents has got something going on the side," Shannon said. She said it as if cheating in a marriage were as common as cars on the highway.

"How can you say that?" I shot back. "First you tell me awful stuff about your mom and now you say one of my parents was fooling around. I don't need this."

"Sorry," Shannon sighed, her voice dropping down. "I forgot what it's like right after the split-up. I guess you're feeling a little touchy."

"Right now, I don't even know how I feel. I wish I could let it out like Jacob. He just throws stuff against the wall," I told her as we got near the front doors of our school.

"*Yah, is gut to verk out feelings of anger,*" she replied. Shannon spoke the words with a German accent, like she was some kind of doctor.

"Listen," she went on. "Seriously. I was reading someplace that a split-up hits you just like one of your parents died. First you're kind of numb, then you start crying, and then you get angry. But sooner or later you get over it, and then you get on with your life, you know? I mean, there's really nothing else you can do except jump off a bridge, and we're both afraid of heights."

There she was, joking again. The whole divorce thing was easy for her. She'd been through it eight years ago, when she wasn't even old enough to understand what was happening. But I knew. I could see how my mom was a wreck, and my dad burst into tears, and how my brother couldn't even sleep.

At home, it seemed like every day would bring me some kind of trouble. There was the day our old Honda wouldn't start and none of us knew how to use jumper cables. There was the day Jacob was sent home from school for fighting, and Mom began crying after she sent him to his room. Then there was the day the "For Sale" sign got put up in front of the house. That really got me upset, but Mom said that it would take a long time to sell. We wouldn't move until the school year was over – at least, that was her promise.

So the three of us tried hard to pretend we could handle all the problems, but that just made it worse. All the little things seemed worse because Dad wasn't there. And even when things went well, it felt as if there was a hole in the middle of any happiness.

It wasn't any better at my dad's place. Jacob and I would go over for the weekend visits, but there was something weird about the time we spent there. Maybe Dad was trying too hard. Or maybe the place was just too small for us. Either way, it felt awkward being there.

Twice, my dad and I tried to talk about why they had split up, but I couldn't get any straight answers from him. Maybe that's why Jacob kept blaming himself for what happened. Or maybe why I kept hoping that Dad and Mom would get back together.

Sometimes Dad would come over to the house to see Mom. Then I'd say to myself, "This is it, he's coming back." But he never did come back to stay, not even for a night. Dad and Mom would talk, then argue, and then he'd leave.

That's when I'd feel really lousy. That's when I'd wish there was something I could do to bring them back together, so we could all be a family again. But they both have lawyers now, and it looks like the lawyers are going to fight it all out.

I tried to talk to Mom about that just before Christmas. The three of us were putting up the tree, and not doing a very good job. It was always my dad who put on the Christmas lights, swearing when the needles stuck in his fingers. Now it was Mom, and she gritted her teeth when the needles hurt her.

"It looks great, Mom," I told her.

"A lot nicer than Dad's tree," Jacob said. "He's just got a little one with no lights or anything."

"I'm surprised he bothered to put one up," Mom said.

"Maybe we could have him here for Christmas dinner," I said. "It's going to be kind of lonely for him in the apartment."

"No, Maddy, I don't think so," Mom told me. My mother was up on a step stool, trying to put the angel on the top of the tree.

"But Mom, it's Christmas – " Jacob whined.

"I know what time of year it is," Mom shot back, "but we've got to get used to doing things by ourselves. Your father's got his own life now – let him enjoy it. You kids will be staying with him the weekend before Christmas. Then he's flying down to Florida with his girlfriend."

"Girlfriend?" I said.

"Oh, I guess he didn't tell you about Elaine," Mom replied. "He didn't tell me either, but I found out. I hear it's been going on for some time," she said, her voice hard and bitter. I knew what she meant. She was saying that Dad had been seeing Elaine even before my parents split up. She was saying that Dad had cheated on her.

"I wish Dad would take *me* to Florida," Jacob said.

I was going to say something, but Mom shot me a look. The look said that we shouldn't talk about this any more, not in front of Jacob.

"Let's work on our own Christmas," Mom said, trying to hook the angel to the top branch. For just a second, she had it – but then the branch tipped and the angel fell.

"It's smashed," Jacob cried.

"No, it's just broken in half," I said, picking up the pieces. "We can glue it back together."

Mom got down off the step stool, looking as if she were going to break down and cry.

"I can glue it – " I said again.

"Oh, Maddy," mom told me. Her eyes were full of hurt, but her mouth was set firm. "When are you going to stop trying to put all the pieces back together?"

Mom wasn't just talking about the angel – she was talking about our broken family.

CHAPTER 4

Don't Be Like That!

The whole holiday was rocky. Jacob was angry all the time. And my mom was always acting real tough, and then losing it. I guess I was so busy thinking about them that I didn't pay much attention to myself.

"How are you?" Shannon would ask.

"I'm fine," I would lie.

And I did seem fine, but really? Really, I was as angry as Jacob. My dad had messed up our nice little family. For what? So when Mom told me about Elaine, the anger inside me started to come out. And there was just one place where I could let it out.

It was about a week before Christmas when my dad showed up to take us to dinner.

"Where are we going tonight, Dad?" Jacob asked my father.

"Out for dinner. But I've got something special to tell you later," Dad said. He was driving his new company car over by the Arena. "It's kind of a Christmas surprise – but I'll let you know about it after we eat."

"Do we have to go out to eat *again?*" I asked him.

That was one of the rotten things about the split-up. When we were still a family, we used to just stay home most nights. But now my dad was always *taking* us somewhere. Maybe his place was a bit small, but that didn't mean we always had to go out. Jacob was getting spoiled from too many Blue Bombers games and bowling alley trips. Sometimes I wished the three of us could just sit around and watch TV, like we used to. But nothing was like it used to be.

"Well, you know how lousy my cooking is, Maddy," he said. "I thought we could maybe go up to that new steak house on Portage. Jacob can get a burger –"

"And French fries," Jacob broke in. "I *love* French fries."

"And we can get some nice steaks. That sure beats my spaghetti, doesn't it?" Dad asked, looking over at me.

How could I say no when he gave me that smile? It had been like that ever since the split-up. When he smiled at Jacob and me, it was like he really needed us to say, "It's all okay."

We stopped at his apartment on the way to the restaurant. In the living room was the fake Christmas tree dad had put up on our old coffee table. Under it were our presents from him. But there were too many of them, and that made it all seem phony.

Maybe the money was another thing that bugged me. Sure, he gave Mom a cheque each month to keep us going, but we never had quite enough to get by. There wasn't any cash for new shoes, or movies, or trips out to restaurants. My mom had to really save hard just to keep up my dance lessons. And here was Dad, a pile of presents under the tree, taking us out to a steak house. Why couldn't he understand? We needed money to live, not just to have a good time.

But we didn't talk about that. We never did. We didn't talk about the split-up, or how Mom was, or how Dad was – or anything important. Instead, we talked about the easy things – our school, his work, Christmas.

"How was the last week at school?" Dad asked.

"We had a party," Jacob said, pigging out on his French fries. "Mrs. Hilroy gave all the kids candy canes – except me. She's a goof."

"Jacob, that's no way to talk," Dad told him. But he was still smiling, like it didn't matter. If either of us had said something like that a year ago, we'd have really gotten it.

"Jacob was in another fight at recess," I told him.

"Look, buddy," my dad began in a stern voice, "I thought you promised to clean up your act."

"The kid threw a snowball and it hit me right in the *eye*."

"That's no reason to get into fights. You should speak to the teacher in charge," Dad went on.

"There was no teacher – " Jacob whined.

"There's always one on duty," I shot back. "You just like getting into fights."

My dad shook his head. "I don't know why you're acting like this, buddy. You never used to get in trouble."

And then there was silence. My dad was right – Jacob never used to get in trouble, not before the split-up. But now Jacob had become a problem. He'd get in fights, "forget" about school trips, talk back to his teachers. We all knew it was because of the split-up, but no one would admit it. None of us could really face the truth.

"What's the surprise?" Jacob asked. He was changing the subject, but that was O.K. with my father.

"Well, it's something that Maddy is going to love – and I think you'll enjoy it too," he said to Jacob.

"Well, what *is* it?" Jacob asked in his bratty voice.

My father was just smiling, like a cat sitting on a case of Miss Mew. "I've got tickets to the ballet," he said proudly, "for the *Nutcracker*. It was all sold out, so I had to ask a friend of mine at work to get hold of some tickets."

"You're kidding," I said. My dad knew that dancing was just about the most important thing in my life.

"But ballet is yucky," Jacob groaned.

"No it's not," Dad tried to explain. "There's great dancing, and toy soldiers who come to life, and a wicked prince – sort of like your crazy comic books, only with music."

Jacob didn't look convinced by what Dad said, but at least he shut up.

"And, believe me, it wasn't easy coming up with four tickets," Dad told us.

"*Four* tickets?" I said. For just a second, I thought maybe he was going to take Mom along with us.

"Well, uh, you see, the friend who managed to get the tickets wants to come, too. And I think maybe it's time you got to meet Elaine."

That's when I froze. As soon as he said "Elaine," I couldn't see the ballet in my mind. The only thing I could see was my mother's face and the angel falling from the tree. I put down my knife and fork and stared at my plate.

It was only my father who kept on talking. "Elaine has been wanting to meet the two of you for some time now. So when she got the ballet tickets, I thought that it might be a good chance for us to get together. It won't be a big deal or anything – "

I guess Dad would have kept on talking if I'd let him, but I didn't.

"I've changed my mind," I said. "I don't want to go. Jacob doesn't want to go either."

"But Maddy, why not?" my father begged. Then there was that smile on his face again, the one that wanted me to say "O.K.," but this wasn't O.K. with me.

"You know why not," I shot back. "Not with Elaine."

"And I don't like stupid dancing, anyhow," Jacob joined in.

"Now look, you guys, I don't want to give orders around here," my father said. "But Elaine went to a lot of trouble to get the tickets."

"Then you two go," I said, "and sell the extra tickets at the door. I'll stay home and look after Jacob."

"I think Jacob will decide if he wants to go with us," my father announced. He was angry now, but didn't know what to do with it.

"Then I can stay at your place by myself, or I can stay home with Mom," I said, staring back at him. "She can't afford to go to Florida or buy tickets to the ballet. But that doesn't mean we can't have a good time – just being together."

"Maddy, don't be like that," my father said.

"I'll be any way I want!" I shouted back. Some people in the restaurant were looking at us, but I didn't care. "I'm not going with Elaine to the ballet, or the movies, or anywhere. Not after what she did to us." I could feel the tears welling up, but I fought them back. "Not after what you two did to us."

Then I ran off, out into the cold winter night.

CHAPTER 5

Who's Getting Hurt?

Shannon had left before Christmas on a holiday with her mom. That made it a week before I could tell her what happened. Then I dumped it all – Elaine, the ballet tickets, my running home.

"Sounds awful," she said.

"But listen," I told her, "don't you dare say 'I told you so.'"

"Sure, I'll just lie and say that Elaine was a big surprise to me, too," Shannon replied.

She was leaning back on her bed, stuffing her face with my Christmas candy. First she'd take a piece of chocolate out of the box. Then she'd tell me she shouldn't eat it because it makes her break out. And then she'd pop it in her mouth.

As for me, I was off candy. Dancers are supposed

to be thin, I told myself, so I was happy to give it to Jacob or Shannon .

"It's so awful," I said.

"That your dad was having an affair?" Shannon asked. "C'mon Maddy, how could we have soap operas if married people were faithful to each other? These things happen."

"But not to real people, not to us," I groaned.

I'd had lots of time to think about it, about my parents and what went wrong. I wondered if Jacob and me had been part of it. Maybe my dad was just bored with the family, or we bugged him too much. Or maybe it was my mom, the way she put him down when he came home from work. Or maybe Elaine just went after him. Maybe she played up to my dad like some of those women on the soap operas. It was hard to imagine anyone chasing after my dad, but it might have happened.

"What makes you think your parents are so much better than anybody else?" Shannon asked. "People are people, and they make mistakes."

"Yeah, yeah," I sighed. "But that doesn't make it

any easier. When Dad told me, I felt like I'd been slapped in the face."

"I know what it's like," Shannon agreed. "I can still remember when my dad, I mean my ex-dad, told me he was moving to New York. Then he mentioned that he wouldn't see me much any more, except maybe summers. He was smiling like I was supposed to say, 'O.K., no problem,' and wish him luck on the new job." Shannon looked upset as she thought back.

"What did you say?" I asked.

"I said, 'O.K., no problem,'" Shannon told me. "And then, when he left, I cried like I'd never cried in my entire life."

We were both quiet. I wondered if our parents would ever really know how we felt. I wondered if they knew the kind of *pain* that you can feel when when a family splits up.

"So anyway," Shannon said, taking another piece of chocolate. "Jacob went to the ballet and you stayed home."

"No, neither one of us went. The kid doesn't like ballet anyhow."

"And what about your dad?" Shannon asked.

"I haven't seen my father since . . . and I don't want to. Jacob can go over there if he wants, but not me."

"Cutting off your nose to spite your face, eh?" Shannon laughed.

"What's that supposed to mean? I shot back.

"It means, who's getting hurt? You stop seeing your dad and feel rotten. He's free to play around with his girlfriend. Your brother gets all sorts of guilt goodies . . . "

"What's a guilt goodie?"

"It's the stuff they give you to make up for not being around. I bet those ballet tickets were the first bit. Just wait till you see everything they dump on your brother. What's that old song, *Money Can't Buy Me Love*? Except I bet it can."

"You're awful," I snapped at her.

"No, just overweight. And I've been through this, remember?"

"I know, the voice of wisdom," I sighed. I went over to the closet and pulled out some old dance shoes. I used to get new ones every couple of months, but not any more.

"So what's the girlfriend like? Any reports from your brother?"

"He says she's 'old' but who knows what that means. Her hair is blond and she wears glasses, and that's about it. All Jacob can say is that she's 'nice,'"

"Well, maybe she is," Shannon replied. "Not all the 'other women' belong on the *Jerry Springer* show."

"How can you say that?" I shot back. "I mean, she was having an affair with my dad – and that broke up the marriage."

"O.K., Maddy, I get the message," Shannon told me. "Maybe this Elaine person did have something going on with your dad. But even my mom will tell you – an affair doesn't make a marriage blow up. Look at that doctor on *Days of Our Lives* . . . "

Sometimes I just can't listen to Shannon go on about people. She seems to think that life is like some big TV soap, where everyone is all mixed up with everyone else. Of course, Shannon was hurt bad when her parents split up and her dad left. Since then, her mom has done pretty well in business, but the rest of her life has been wild. My mom used to say that Shannon 's mom changed boyfriends the way we might change dishrags – and just as often. So when Shannon says, "What's normal?" it's a real question for her. She just doesn't know.

But I can still remember what normal was like.

Normal was the four of us – Mom, Dad, Jacob and me – on Christmas morning. Mom would be sleepy from having wrapped all the gifts. My dad would be in his bathrobe, sipping eggnog as he watched us. Jacob would rip the paper off all his presents in five minutes. I'd space mine out so they'd last at least an hour or so. It used to be so nice, the four of us, all cuddled together on Christmas morning.

Now all that was finished – and it would soon get worse.

CHAPTER 6

An Offer on the House

So I danced. I've loved dancing ever since I was little. Now I did jazz and ballet dancing, both. Some kids can stick with ballet because they've got big talent. But big talent wasn't what I had. I just loved the dancing.

Mrs. Taylor was my teacher, and she was really nice to me during all this. She opened the studio during Christmas week so I'd have some place to dance. And she never minded me coming in after school to practice. Her studio felt like a lot nicer place than my house most days.

As I danced, I watched myself in the mirror. It was the only way I could find the me that I'd been before the split-up. These days, we were all so phony. We kept on acting like everything was okay, but it wasn't. Jacob got in fights in school. My mom would burst into tears for no reason. My marks on the last report card were all down. The only person who seemed in good shape was my dad. But, of course, he had his new girlfriend to help him through it all.

I was practicing after school one day when Mrs. Taylor came up to me.

"Maddy, are you okay?" she asked.

"Sure," I said, "except this one leg hurts a little. I think I twisted it."

"No," Mrs. Taylor went on, "that's not what I mean. I mean, are you *really* okay? I have a hunch what your family is going through, and it must be tough."

"No, I'm fine," I told her, holding still for a second. "I mean, my dad was bugging me, but now I don't see him so it's no problem."

"You don't see him," she asked, "at all?"

"Well, I don't do the visit every other week like Jacob does. Dad's got his girlfriend and all, so why bother?" I sounded so easy with all this, as if I really didn't care.

"Maybe you should be glad your dad got a new

girlfriend," Mrs. Taylor went on. "Sooner or later, your mom will get a new boyfriend, too. Life goes on, you know."

"Yeah, I know," I said. I felt a funny feeling in my chest, a strange kind of hurt.

"There's no sense being angry with either of them," Mrs. Taylor said. She sighed and did a stretch. "Your mom and dad are just doing the best they can. You can't really blame them, or yourself, or the girlfriend, or anybody."

"I guess not," I told her. But that was a lie. I blamed my dad and Elaine for what happened. I blamed him for not loving my mom, and not keeping our little family in one piece. I blamed him a lot.

"Maddy, I can tell you don't believe me," Mrs. Taylor said, "but it's true. I know about these things."

"You do?" I asked.

"Yeah," she said, looking at herself in the mirror. "A long time ago . . . I was the girlfriend."

That was a shocker. I knew that Mrs. Taylor had been married once before. And I knew she was married now. But who knew what kind of mess had gone on in between? Who knew if she were playing around with somebody else's husband. Adults! They keep pretending that they're grown-ups, but I kind of wonder.

It was after a dance workout in February that I came home to another shock. My mom was pacing around the house. She had a cup of coffee in one hand, a piece of paper in the other.

"Good news," Mom said, smiling at me.

"What's that?" I asked her, hanging up my coat.

"We've had an offer on the house," she said. "It's two thousand less than what we wanted, but I'm tired of having people slop through here. Besides, the agent says it's a lousy time of year to list any house and – "

"What are you trying to say?" I broke in.

My mom looked at me and let me have it, straight – "I'm selling the house."

One more explosion, one more bomb blowing up the life that I used to know.

"You're not asking," I said, "you've decided."

My mom looked down into her coffee, then up at me.

"Yes, I have," she said, looking very sure of herself. "Maddy, it's time for us to move on. We can't keep waiting around here as if our old life is going to pick up again. That's finished, for good, and we have to go on to the next thing."

"So you're taking the offer," I said, finishing up for her.

She nodded. "The sale closes in two months, at

the end of April, and we're going to move. I've made up my mind."

"But what about me and Jacob?" I shouted. "You've made up your mind, but what about us? You didn't ask us when you put the house up for sale, you just did it. And now you're selling our home out from under us. Why? Because 'you've made up your mind!' Well, thanks a lot."

"Maddy, don't you dare use that tone of voice with me."

"I'll use any tone of voice I want," I screamed. "After what you and dad have done to me . . ." and then I ran out of words. I was so angry and so upset that I couldn't even cry.

Two months! She had promised that we wouldn't move until school was finished and now – two months! She had lied to me, betrayed my trust – just like dad.

CHAPTER 7

Moving Day

Just before moving day, we had enough junk out on the lawn to fill a city garbage truck. Some of the junk was easy to sort – old clothes, broken toys, Aunt Shirley's old La-Z Boy chair. But what about my very first ballet dress? Well, we kept that. But we threw out all the beat-up ballet shoes, and my old skateboard, and the Scrabble set that was missing a Q. It seemed, sometimes, like we were throwing out a whole life.

"Well, at least you're going to stay close," Shannon said. She was eating a candy bar that had been stuck under my bed, maybe for years.

"Yeah," I agreed. Our new apartment was only three blocks away. "And the new place makes more sense since we don't need all this space any more."

"That's what my mom says sometimes," Shannon

told me. "But if we sell the house, I guess a chunk of money goes to my ex-dad. So it looks like we're stuck."

"Well, moving sure isn't fun," I told her, pushing a filled box toward the door.

"It comes with a split-up," Shannon said. "We got off easy because my mom had a good job already. Otherwise we'd have been dirt poor."

"I already know about dirt poor. I had to beg my dad to keep paying for my jazz dance lessons, and you know how I felt about that."

Shannon gave me a funny look and said, "Dirt poor isn't when you can't pay for dance lessons, Maddy. It's when you can't pay for *food*."

"It could come to that, too," I told her, "unless Mom gets a job."

My dad's support cheque wasn't big enough to keep the three of us going, even in a rented apartment. So far, Mom had been using our savings to help us get by. But now the savings were almost gone, and her lawyer wanted some money, and we were in trouble. My dad had enough cash to take his girlfriend to Florida, but soon we'd be down to dinners of hot dogs and beans. It wasn't fair. None of it was fair.

I guess that's what I was feeling when I saw dad the day we moved. My dad came over to our house to get some stuff he'd left behind. It had been over six months since he moved out. Now it felt strange to have Dad in the house at all.

Dad and Mom tried hard to stay away from each other that day. When they had to talk, it was icy cold and polite. Mom spent her time upstairs, in the bedrooms. She had piled up most of my dad's stuff down in the basement, near his old workshop.

My dad was busy packing up all the tools and sorting out *his* CDs and *his* books. Jacob was down there with him, goofing around. And I was mostly someplace in between. When I heard my dad close up his tool box, I went downstairs to talk to him.

"Dad, I don't think you should take all the tools with you," I said.

He looked up at me as I stood there. "I've made up a little tool kit for your mom," he said, his voice quiet. Off in one corner, Jacob was zooming some cars along the concrete floor.

"Yeah, but you're taking the Skil saw and the power drill, and maybe we'll need them."

"All your mother has to do is call up and ask," he told me. "Or maybe she should go out and buy her own."

"Using what for money?" I asked.

"She gets support from me, enough to keep you going," he said, as if it were true.

"Dad, if your support were enough, we wouldn't have to move," I told him.

57

"It's what I can afford, Maddy," he said, giving me one of his *looks*. "I need money to live, too, though your mother's lawyer doesn't seem to think so."

"Then how come you can go off to Florida while we have to sell the house?" I threw back at him. "How come you've got a new car and we haven't got enough money for clothes?"

"It's a company car, Maddy," Dad said, his voice rising. "And I don't have to explain *my* money to a fourteen-year-old. Your mother can solve all her money problems just by getting some work."

"That's right, Maddy," Jacob said, getting on Dad's side. "Even Mom says she's going to get a job."

Dad joined in. "I don't make nearly enough money – "

I cut him off. "There always used to be enough money, back before you split up. But now it's all messed up, all because . . ."

My dad came over and tried to put his arm around me, but I shrugged it off. "All because of me," my dad finished for me. "Sounds like you've been listening to your mother."

"I hate it!" I shouted. "I hate it the way you two can't even talk to each other, and the way the stupid lawyers make everything worse!"

Even Jacob was nodding his head, agreeing with me for a change. Here we were, moving out of the house where I'd spent almost my entire life, and my dad wasn't helping. He was only worried about *his* stuff, *his* life – and trying to pretend that none of it was his fault.

"I'm sorry, Maddy, but there are some things I just can't change," my dad said.

"But you can leave the power drill," I told him.

"Okay, I'll bring it back after the move. I'm putting up some new bookshelves for Elaine – "

I just stared at my father. How could he even say her name in our house? "Is Elaine that much more important than your family?" I asked him.

"I didn't say that," my dad pleaded. "It's just that I promised to help her – "

I wouldn't let him finish. "So you can put up

shelves for Elaine, but you can't help us in *our* move, can you?"

"Your mom doesn't want any help," Dad said.

"She doesn't want *your* help," I told him. I was shouting, but I didn't care. "Not after what you've done to us."

"Maddy, that's not fair," my dad said.

"What do you know about *fair?*" I spat out. "What do you care about how we feel? You've got Elaine and your place and your car and your trips – why do you need us any more?"

My dad looked like somehow he was the one who was hurt. "Maddy, I'll always need you. Just because your mom and I can't live together doesn't mean you aren't important."

"And me, too," Jacob piped up.

"Of course you, too," my dad added quickly, smiling down at my brother. "Listen, Maddy, I know this is tough for you. Your mom was telling me how you blew up at her the other day, so I know you're angry."

"I've got every reason to be angry," I shouted.

"You'd be angry too if everything you had in life just blew up in front of your face."

"Kaboom!" Jacob said, smashing two cars together. My father and I didn't even look at him.

"Maddy," my dad went on, "you've got to get over it. Your mom and I are trying to get on with our lives. You should too."

"Well maybe I don't want to," I shouted. "Maybe my life ended the day you walked out of here so you could be with your girlfriend."

Then I went storming up the stairs and over to Shannon's house. I couldn't take any more – no more of him, no more of the moving, no more of anything.

CHAPTER 8

"You Just Don't Understand"

So I danced. While everything else was falling apart all around me, I danced.

It's hard to explain why the dancing was so important to me. Of course, there was the music – some classical, some old songs by James Taylor and some new stuff by Pearl Jam and Ricky Martin. But it was more than that. It was more than the steps and the body movement. It was how I felt when I was moving to the music. I felt whole, like a real person. When I danced, I was the Maddy McCulloch I had been before . . . before the split-up.

Of course, there were other reasons, too. Mrs. Taylor, my dance teacher, was the only person in the world who made me feel good about myself. She told me how much I was improving with all the practice I got. Then, in March, she picked me to join her adult dancers for a special show. For two days I was walking on air. Me – a real dancer! Me – going to dance at Centennial Concert Hall!

All that meant a lot of practice. I practiced six days a week on my own, two or three times with the other dancers. But I loved the time I spent at the studio. It was small and crowded, but there was always music and it felt like home. After we moved to the apartment, it felt like the only real home I had.

I had never lived in an apartment before, and if felt strange. There was a lobby instead of a front porch and a long hall that always smelled like someone else's supper. The apartment itself seemed kind of empty. Often there was no one there.

My mother had got a job at the real estate office with Shannon's mom. She worked until six most days. Jacob spent the time after school at a friend's place down the street. I practiced after school. So the place was empty most of the time. It was as if none of us really wanted to be there.

On weekends, my brother would go off to Dad's place and Mom sometimes went to work. That was when the apartment really felt strange. Sometimes I'd be there, alone, staring at these strange bare walls. I wondered how it happened. How we ended up living here with our lives going off every which way.

But I knew the answer – it was Elaine, and Dad, and the split-up. When my mid-term marks came in, I had dropped down to C's. I knew why, of course. I never blamed anyone out loud. I never gave Jacob a hard time when he came back from Dad's. But I knew who had ruined our family.

All through that spring and summer, my mom and dad hardly talked to each other. They had lawyers now, and the lawyers did all the talking for them. My dad's lawyer tried to cut back on support now that Mom was working. My mom's lawyer said that we needed more money because my mom was just starting a career.

And there were all sorts of other things to fight over. When was my mom going to get her share of the house money? Who really owned our old car?

How long would Jacob go to Dad's for the summer? Sometimes I thought – *why can't they just sit down and talk it out?* But they weren't really talking, and I wasn't talking much either. The lawyers were talking for all of us.

It was May when Jacob and I got our own lawyer. It seemed strange at the time. I guess when the parents get close to divorce, the government starts to worry about the kids. By then, of course, it's too late. But Jacob and I still had to go visit this lawyer, a fat old guy named Michael Bergman, to tell him we were doing O.K. That's what I explained to Shannon when we got back.

"He just sort of sat there," I said. "He played with his beard while I told him I was doing just fine. I felt like I was going to a shrink."

"Who is this lawyer guy?" Shannon asked. "What do they call him?"

"The Official Guardian, like I was some kind of orphan," I said.

"Well, if you were in some real trouble," Shannon said, "at least you'd have someone on your side. I should have called mine when Mom was living with Bob and fighting all the time. Dad was off in the States and I had nobody."

"It must have been bad," I said.

Shannon was staring off into space with a funny look on her face. "Sometimes, I'd hear them fight and I'd think, 'What if Bob kills my mom, what then?' I'd get so scared, and there was nobody I could tell, not even you."

"Well, you could have –"

Shannon cut me off. "Sure, maybe I *could* have talked about it then, and I am talking about it now. But when you're seven or eight, it's hard to find the right words. It's hard not to think that somehow it's all your fault, and if you tell someone else, it will all get worse." When Shannon stopped talking, the room seemed very quiet.

"I didn't know," I said.

"That's why I keep telling you – you've got it easy," Shannon said, pulling back out of her memories. "I mean, yeah, you were poor for a while and, sure, it cost you a house. But you've still got your family here in the city and no dumb boyfriends to worry about. You've got your dancing and this big show coming up. The only real problems you've got are the ones you're making up for yourself."

"What's that crack supposed to mean?" I asked.

Shannon got up and pulled some gum out of her dresser, tossing one stick to me. "You know what it means," she said.

"My father," I answered.

"Yeah, your father and this thing you've got against Elaine. I mean, you've never even met her, so it's really kind of crazy."

"Well, you don't know," I said, hugging my knees.

"Neither do you," Shannon said. "You think your dad was having an affair with Elaine and that split up the family. But you don't *know* that for sure. You don't know if your dad was really playing around. You don't know if your mother was rotten to him, or kept on cutting him down, or was having an affair herself."

"I don't have to listen to this," I snapped back.

"Wait, I didn't mean it like that," Shannon said as I got up. "I'm just saying that kids don't really know what goes on in a marriage. I mean, my

dad was a drunk, but I never knew that until a long time after he left. What do we *really* know about our parents anyhow? And what makes you so sure that your dad caused the split-up?"

"Well, I can figure it out," I said.

"But how do you *know*, Maddy? Because your mom says so? If I believed all the stuff my mom says about my dad, I'd expect to see him charged with murder. But I'll never find out the truth, because he's gone. He's right out of my life, and there's nothing I can do about that. I don't even have his phone number, you know that?"

Shannon seemed almost ready to cry, but so was I.

"Maybe you're better off," I mumbled.

"See, there you go," Shannon exploded. "That's you being crazy again. I mean, the split-up is bad enough and you make the whole thing worse by cutting off your dad. What are you trying to do? Punish him – or punish yourself?"

"Shannon – he was having an affair," I said.

"And so was my mom when Dad left," Shannon threw back at me, "but that doesn't mean I don't love her. You can't live the rest of your life always blaming people. I mean, if I just had a chance to see my dad, just once, I'd go for it so fast your head would spin. And you – you won't even go have dinner with your dad when he begs you to come over. You're just crazy – "

I think I could have been really mad at Shannon for all that, but she was crying now, and I knew she was crying for herself more than for me. I felt bad for her, and for me too, so I couldn't blow up at her.

I said softly, "You just don't understand," and held her as she cried.

Except, of course, she really did understand. A lot better than I did.

CHAPTER 9

I've Missed You

I practiced like crazy for our big show in July. The symphony had hired our Judith Taylor Dancers for one of their summer concerts. We were doing a modern ballet to go with some music by Bach. We knew that a couple thousand people would be there to see us. That's ten times as many as ever came out to one of our studio recitals. And we were ten times as nervous.

So I practiced. We all practiced.

Step, back, step, bend . . . graceful . . . turn to right, hand up . . .

There were all these moves to remember. If even one of us made a mistake, it all fell apart. For fifteen minutes on stage, we must have spent a thousand hours getting ready. No one ever sees all the work. But it was so important to me, to Mrs.

Taylor, to all of us. We wanted to get it perfect, to make it beautiful.

The last week, we went to practice with the orchestra. The first time, it was awful. They played too slow, slower than the tape, or maybe we were nervous and our timing was off. Mrs. Taylor got upset with us and then with the orchestra. But the second time it was better, and the dancing looked pretty good. And by the third time, it felt good – Mrs. Taylor said it was "great" and we were ready.

I was putting on my make-up in the change room when I saw Shannon's face in the mirror. Only Shannon would be pushy enough to come backstage like that.

"What are you doing here?" I said. Then a flash went off in my face. The older dancers were staring at her and I felt embarrassed.

"I want a picture to prove I knew you back when you were just getting started," Shannon said proudly. "Here, you want to see?" She turned her digital camera so I could see a shot of me with my mouth wide open.

The whole line of dancers just laughed.

"Look, I've got to get my make-up on," I said, my face turning red.

"I know – I just wanted to get the picture and wish you good luck," Shannon said. Then she went on, in a lower voice, "By the way, I saw your dad out in the lobby."

"What's he doing here?" I grumbled.

"Maybe he cares about you, or something weird like that." Shannon said. "But this is no time to talk about it. Good luck, or . . . uh, break a leg." Shannon smiled when she saw the look on my face. "I guess that's not what you're supposed to say to ballet dancers, is it?"

The dancer next to me laughed, and then Shannon was gone. I was feeling more nervous than ever. All of the dancers were on edge, even those who'd been in the company for years. We made dumb jokes, and tried to laugh, and tried to cover up how we really felt. Scared – that's how I really felt – so keyed up I felt like I was going to explode.

It seemed like hours before we went up to the stage and then . . . then we were on. Dancing. The lights burned down at me and I couldn't see the audience. There was no time to see, anyhow. Only time to dance.

Step, back, step, bend . . . graceful . . . turn to right, hand up . . .

I was afraid for only the first few seconds, then I was caught up in the dancing. Sure, there were two thousand people out there, but I wasn't dancing for them. I was dancing for me. I wanted at least this one thing in my life to be beautiful. In a world where so much else was messed up, I wanted this dance to be perfect.

Maybe it was. When the music was over and we took our bow, the applause came in waves. Even the players in the orchestra tapped their bows and smiled at us. Three curtain calls! That's how good we were.

So when it was over, when the make-up was off and we were all going to a party, I was still glowing. We'd been "wonderful," that's what Mrs. Taylor said. She'd never been so proud of us – and we'd never been so proud of ourselves.

Mom, Jacob and Shannon met me at the stage door as I came out.

"You were fantastic!" Shannon cried out.

"Just as graceful as the older dancers," my mom said. "And you're only fourteen."

"Oh, Mom – " I said.

They were all talking at once. Shannon kept on about how great it was, and Mom about how I danced like a pro. Even Jacob said it was pretty good. It was while they were all talking that I saw him waiting off at the side. Way outside the group.

It was my dad, all by himself.

I guess when I first saw him, I didn't really know what to do. Part of me wanted him to go away, so I could just enjoy the glow I felt inside. But another part of me was glad he was there, to see the finest moment in my whole life.

But the more I looked at my dad, the more he seemed kind of sad. My father stood there, alone, shut out of all this. That wasn't fair either – not when I felt this good, not when everything was going so well.

I pulled away from the others and went over to him, not sure what to say or do. It had been months since I stopped going over to his place, so we were both awkward.

"Dad . . . " I began.

"Maddy, you were terrific," he said. "I just wanted to say that."

He was standing there with his arms open, looking at me. Then, I'm not really sure how it happened, his arms went around me. And my arms went around him. And we were hugging each other for the first time in a long, long time.

"Daddy, I've missed you," I cried.

"And I've missed you," he said. I could tell from his voice that my father was crying too.

But that was O.K. for both of us, because they were the right kind of tears. They weren't tears of hate and blame any more. They were tears full of love – and that's what we both really needed.

CHAPTER 10

Shannon's Call

All that was a year ago. I won't pretend that it's been easy since then, but it's been better.

The toughest part of the year was meeting Elaine. My dad didn't push it at first, even when I started to spend weekends at his place again. So I put the meeting off until the spring. Then Shannon and my dad both got on my case, so I had to give in. My dad cooked his not-so-great meatballs, and Elaine sat down for supper with the three of us.

I guess it wasn't so bad. It's funny how I had built her up in my mind. I though of her like some kind of witch who had stolen my dad away. In fact, Elaine turned out to be nothing special. She isn't young or sexy, or good-looking. She's just a 35-year-old single mom, who works in my

dad's office. In a funny way, she's a lot like my mom.

Shannon says I blamed Elaine for the split-up so I didn't have to blame my parents. Maybe she's right. Maybe their marriage wasn't that good all along. Maybe my dad changed when he got the sales job. Or maybe my mom just stopped liking him. The truth is, kids never pay much attention to their parents until something goes wrong. And there's not much we can do even then.

Now that the divorce is final, Mom and Dad are talking to each other. All the fights about money and the car and who gets the kids when – those are over. Mom got the car, Dad got his old desk, and the house money got split down the middle. Mom is doing so well at her job that she might even buy a new house. The only thing that's holding her back is her boyfriend.

Mom met this guy, Sam, at work. And Sam thinks she should put her money in the stock market. Now Mom doesn't know what to do about Sam, or the house, or the money. But she's happy – and so are we.

These days I feel like I've pretty much gotten past the split-up. For too long, I spent too much time worrying and hoping and hating. But all of it was about them. It was about things that I couldn't change.

Now I can get back to my own life. There's my dancing, of course, and that's still the most important thing. But I've tried out for the musical at school, and there's this guy in my math class who likes me. It's nice to be able to worry about teenage-stuff again and leave the adult-stuff to my parents.

Just when I felt things were under control around here, Shannon came by with some big news.

"I found out where my father is," she said. I knew she was serious because she didn't call him "my ex-dad" the way she often did.

"Did he call you or something?" I said.

"No, I looked him up on the Internet," Shannon told me. "I thought about e-mailing him, but figured he could just duck out on that. So I made a long-distance call to Florida. His landlady told me he got kicked out of his apartment, lost his job and moved to Denver."

"Nice," I said.

"Now I don't know what to do," Shannon said. "I've got this Denver number and I want to call him, but I'm kind of scared. I mean, maybe he's embarrassed about losing his job. And he never was much good at keeping in touch . . ."

Shannon paused before she got to her biggest question. "And what if he doesn't want to talk to me?"

"Then at least you gave it a try," I said, hoping to give her some courage. "I mean, you don't see him now, so it's not like it would change anything very much."

"Yeah, but I like to *think* that he misses me, you know? And if he hangs up on me or something, well, I'll die."

"He wouldn't do that," I said. "Now give me the number and I'll dial it for you."

"No, I'll dial it myself," Shannon said proudly, "but you stay here, just in case . . ."

She picked up the telephone and punched in the numbers. There were a few seconds while she waited for the phone to ring, and then someone answered at the other end.

"Hello . . . ," Shannon began. "I, uh, want to speak to Mr. James Stokes, uh, is this the right number?"

There was a pause while a voice answered. Shannon's hand was gripping the phone so tight that her knuckles were white.

"James Stokes?" she went on. "This is, uh, this is Shannon . . . you know, your daughter."

For just a second, there was a look of panic on Shannon's face. The guy on the other end must have been asking a question.

"It's really me, Dad," Shannon replied.

I held my breath. I so wanted this to go well for her.

Then the look on Shannon's face grew softer. "Well, don't start crying, Dad, I just called to . . . you mean you're glad? And you've tried to call me? Well, of course we have an unlisted number," Shannon said, smiling now.

That's when I left Shannon's bedroom and went out to the hall. She didn't need me with her any more. Nor did Shannon need me at spring break when she flew down to be with her dad in Denver. By then, we'd been through it all again and again.

We decided she should greet her father with a smile, no matter what she felt. Because we'd learned a few things. Like how she needed a father more than a long-term grudge. Like how parents can screw up, but it doesn't do any good to blame them or get angry. Like the way kids have to make their own lives, because marriages break up and houses get sold. But love can last, we found out, if only you let it.

Here are some other titles you might enjoy:

Tag Team by PAUL KROPP

Jes had plenty of problems to start with. He was short, shy and lonely – at least until he went out for the school's wrestling team. Then his life seemed to turn around – until he had to deal with Banjo and Joey down in the tunnel.

Street Scene by PAUL KROPP

The guys were looking for trouble. Maybe Jamal did pick the wrong girl to dance with. But did that give Sal and his gang an excuse to come after them. The fight should never have started – and it should never have finished the way it did.

Paul Kropp

Scarface by PAUL KROPP

Coming to Canada had been a great thing for Tranh. This was a country of peace and wealth and happiness. So why did Martin Beamis keep picking on him? Did this rich kid have nothing better to do than make life rotten for someone who had already suffered so much?